GW00650004

UNDER
BLACK VEN

Lyme from the Church Cliffs

UNDER BLACK VEN

MARY ANNING'S STORY

JUDITH STINTON

She sells sea-shells on the sea shore;
The shells that she sells are sea-shells I'm sure.
So if she sells sea-shells on the sea shore,
I'm sure that the shells are sea-shore shells.

DORSET BOOKS

First published in 1995 by Dorset Books

Copyright © 1995 Judith Stinton

ISBN 1 87116 423 0

British Library Cataloguing-in-Publication Data
CIP Catalogue Record for this book is available from the British Library

DORSET BOOKS
Official Publisher to Dorset County Council
Halsgrove House
Lower Moor Way
Tiverton EX16 6SS
Telephone 01884 243242
Facsimile 01884 243325

Printed and bound in Great Britain by Bookcraft Ltd.

for Anna

CONTENTS

CHAPTER ONE

They say it was the lightning changed me.

B EFORE THAT DAY, the day of the lightning (which was the nineteenth of August, in the year of 1800), I had been as plump as a dumpling, and about as clever.
Mother hadn't minded my slowness, my health alone was her concern, for I was a sickly child.

The lightning was my first memory. I don't remember the earlier part of the day, except from what I have since been told. I was, after all, but fifteen months of age.
My nurse had taken me to see the horse-jumping round in the Rack Field, both to amuse me, and to give me air.
There was little enough air, though, for the summer's day felt hot and sultry. The horses toiled about the field, almost refusing to jump. The spectators sat on grass which was parched and worn as an old wig. I couldn't yet walk, so my nurse dandled me on her knees, tapping my face and singing:

> *Brow brinky*
> *Eye winky*
> *Chin choppy*
> *Nose noppy*
> *Cheek cheery*
> *Mouth merry*

Merry my mouth was not, I was crying; the day had been long and over-warm. I wanted to go home. Yet my nurse was unwilling to leave – while the jumping still continued she, like all the others, was determined to remain. There was a distant shift of thunder, but still no one moved.

The storm came on suddenly. The sky turned a leafy green, and a fitful wind rattled the branches of the elm trees bordering the great Rack Field. There were a few small drops of rain.

The horses were becoming uneasy. They had to be soothed and led away as the lightning struck, and the thunder came straight after. Holding me tightly in her arms, my nurse ran to take shelter under the ellems. Beside her sheltered two others, Fanny Fowler and Martha Drowes, neither of them older than fifteen years.

I am sure I remember the lightning. How could I forget? It struck the tree which sheltered us, struck all of us, going through me like a shocking blow. The lightning flared so much that I was almost blinded. Then I fell lifeless to the ground (though I remember nothing of that hour).

At first they thought that I was dead, as dead as the other three women. My nurse was dead: her name was Elizabeth Haskin. She, with Fanny Fowler and Martha Drowes, lies buried at the top of the churchyard, between the old plague pit and the crumbling cliff edge. I expect in my lifetime the grave will fall. The sea will take it, and take the church, too.

Yet I was chosen to stay alive. They carried me, as if dead, home to my distraught mother. She washed me, sponged me in the warm water which brought me back to life (the lightning had left me grimy as a sweep). I was quickened; I had been through fire.

Chapter Two

'**M**Y TURN for the rocking horse,' my brother Joseph said. He was a wild and reckless rocker of horses. When he rode, the horse-hair mane flew back towards him, and the fixed joints creaked.

I could not deny him. Unwillingly I slid to the ground, stroking the horse's wooden nose, carved by Father's own hand.

'Don't take too long,' I said (though I knew that once mounted he would ride forever, rocking faster and faster until the horse looked likely to overturn).

He had already begun to gallop. I walked away to sit in the window where I watched the rain slither down the glass. I pressed my nose to the tiny cold panes. Through the flawed glass, streaked with rain, I could see a crooked world. Each pane held a separate segment of smoking sea. Our house was on the dizzy edge of the water. A tall thin house, its feet were often wet.

From below us, in the cellar, came a sound of hammering. A slow, wood-pecking tap, tap, tap, an accompaniment to the more rapid creaking of Joseph on his horse.

Woodshavings: that is the first smell I can remember. Their crisp and spicy scent filled the whole house. Father was a carpenter by trade, and as times then were good, he would work in the cellar both night and day. Father could do anything. He could make a whole roomful of furniture – or some finicky repair for a summer visitor.

And he had made the rocking horse on which Joseph rode so wildly. I ran to tug at the runaway head of the heavy wooden horse.

'I want my turn,' I said, raising my voice a little. If my mother heard me from the floor above, I knew she might come to intervene.

'Give your little sister a turn, Joseph,' she would say, and then he would be forced to dismount.

Joseph left the horse good-humouredly. He ran across to the window and looked at the rain on the sea. 'What shall I do next?' he asked – of no one in particular.

'Come and help me, boy,' called Father from his cellar. 'I need another hand.'

I thought that then I might have my second ride. But before I had even begun it, Joseph had reappeared.

'I'm off on an errand,' he said proudly. 'Would you care to accompany me?'

Together we walked up Broad Street, Joseph and I. My brother was carrying a chair. We both were wearing our hats and boots, and we had the chair for shelter. The street was a steep one, curving and climbing away from the shore. At our side, rain-water gushed down a gulley, shooting towards the sea. The rain had stopped by now, and a pale sun streaked the sky. The cobbles shone like fishes' scales. Joseph paused to catch his breath from time to time, and rested on the chair. At Sherborne Lane we gratefully turned, down to the new-built houses below, their thatch still bright and stiff.

Old Curtis's house was Number 6. He sat usually in the window, watching the builders and the gossips of the street. He was there today, and saw us coming from the top part of the lane.

'Come in,' he shouted. 'Quickly, mind.' We entered the stuffy room and Joseph set the mended chair down in front of him. Sam Curtis lifted it with one strong hand and examined the splinted leg. Then he nodded. From the mantelpiece he took a chipped milk jug, powdered with roses, in which he kept his money. 'Six, seven, eight,' he counted. I was carefully watching. ('He's not to be trusted,' Mother had warned me.)

'Would you try it for me, Mary?' Old Curtis asked suddenly.

'There'll be nothing wrong with Father's repairs...' I began, as he held out the chair towards me.

'If you wish it,' I dutifully began to sit – to sit upon thin air. I landed slam! upon the floor as he pulled the chair away. Old Curtis bellowed like a triumphant bull, but I did not cry out.

'Are you injured, Mary?' Joseph helped me to my feet. He was smiling. My back was jarred, my eyes were tearful.

'Don't get tilty now, you must learn to take a joke,' Sam Curtis roared. 'Young maids must be a-smiling.'

I tried to smile, but I could not. Business over, Old Curtis was anyways talking to Joe. His jest was quite forgotten.

'I'm glad to see this old chair again,' Sam Curtis said. 'I had it in my first house – the one that was down in Coombe Street bottom. 'Tisn't there any longer. Some fifty years since, the roof went a-sliding into the street, the chimney and all. Course, we couldn't live there after that. We took the street door with us, and the furniture too. I've always kept that chair, as I was the one that found it...'

I could not prevent myself. 'Found it?' I enquired.

He transferred his attention back to me. 'Yes, 'twas I that found it, down on Back Beach, one morning when fishing was over. We'd not been lucky at fishing that day. There was a cruel sea, with little sign of a catch. I was feeling chilled through to the bone... Well, this old chair must have come from a wreck. There she sits, in the sand, alongside a table and three other chairs like her, all upright and looking for a new master. The others were in pieces, but I gave this one a home, and here she be, back again to share my house.'

Chairs in the sand indeed. I thought him an old liar. I had little interest then in what came from the sea. Fire, not water, had been my element.

FIRE AT LYME REGIS.

Chapter Three

B UT IN LYME the sea could never be quite forgotten. It would make its presence felt at some unexpected turn. The tides were unpredictable. Though fire would sometimes flare in the town (I remember in my childhood one great conflagration), leaving gaunt hulks for houses, yet fire was never near so frightening. We were subject most of all to the moods of the sea.

One winter's evening, we went to bed early. The room was too cold to sit around in, for the fire was low and we were short of coal. Our fire was fed with sea-coal, picked by Joseph and me from the beach, coal which had been washed up from north-country coasters in stormy weather. The sea had been peaceful lately, and we had found no coal. Neither of us cared for the coal-gathering, which meant wading in the shallows of an often icy sea, delving in the waves for the slimy black lumps. On the last occasion when we had been to pick it, we had gathered only enough to cover the bottom of a sack.

Our attic bedroom felt warmer by far than the down-stairs rooms. Mother came to bid us goodnight.

'Please read us a story,' we begged. 'Read us a story.' Sometimes Mother would read us a Bible chapter. We had no other book in the house.

'I hope it *is* a story,' Joseph whispered as Mother opened the holy book. Occasionally a chapter would be a register of names or pages of laws, but Mother read them just the same.

What chapter did we have that night? I think it was the account of a battle. What it should have been was the story of Noah and his Ark.

Mother wished us goodnight and we lay still, waiting until the sound of her footsteps had faded away. She had left us the candle, as it was nearly at its end. The shadow shapes we made with our hands shuddered across the slanting walls as the candle leapt and guttered. I made a crocodile, snout a-snapping, but dropped my hands in horror as his shape loomed closer. Joseph's monkey-shape skittered along the ceiling, growing suddenly as large as a man.

Out went the candle, and we lay down to sleep.
The room was quiet, but I could not settle. The window panes were rattling in their frames, and I could hear the waves far below. (They were always below us, but I mostly did not hear them.)

It was surprising, then, that I did not wake sooner – I, who did not think that I would ever sleep at all. What woke me was a different sound: the sound of water not just slapping, overflowing into the cellar, as it sometimes did at high tide. This was a noise like that of an animal, a wild beast approaching in great wrath.

'Joe!' I shouted, but Joe was already awake. He was staring towards the door, as if it might be a-bursten wide by the ravings of the sea.

Now the door did open – and Father entered. As he opened the door the sound of the sea grew louder.
He was carrying a swaying lantern.

He spoke, but so quietly that I couldn't hear the murmur of his voice. I strained my ears to listen.

'The sea has broken in,' Father said. 'But don't be frightened. Just stay where you are, in bed.'

He glanced over his shoulder – was he really expecting that the sea would come so close? Then Mother appeared behind him. They sat down together on the woollen coverlet.

Joseph fidgeted. 'Mightn't we be safer in the street?' he asked.

'Maybe so, but I fear we cannot reach the street,' Father said. 'The sea has swept the staircase away.'

'We'll drown, then,' Joseph cried. I looked at Father. 'If need be,' Father says, 'We'll climb on to the roof.'

All night long the water beat against the house, until I thought the walls must fall into the sea, taking us with them as they fell. The sound was deafening, but the waters did not rise further. By dawn it was plain that the tide was receding, and we all four fell asleep on the bed, wearied by a night of watching.

We awoke to the stench of tidal mud, a stink as strong as that of rotten eggs. There was a banging on the attic window. It was our neighbours, the Dollins, come to our rescue with a ladder. As Mother half-opened the window the stench grew stronger. 'Come, Mary,' she said, pushing me before her. Eyes tightly closed, I was hauled on to the ladder, and so was the first to reach the ground, to put my feet into that treacherous mud. Joe and I were both holding our noses, while Mother refused to enter her half-wrecked house. Only Father risked an entry, grubbing in the cellar for his buried chest of tools.

''Twill be a pity if they are lost,' he said.

CHAPTER FOUR

Mud, mud, mud, mud. Try as we might, over the succeeding weeks, we could not rid ourselves of the mud. It reappeared overnight in the scoured corners of rooms, just as toadstools might have, or a spider's web. Father found his tools, safely embedded in the soft mud inside his tool chest, but somehow they no longer seemed to work so well. Mud stained the floorboards and left its mark on the walls.

We were not the only ones to be affected. In the Cockmoile prison which was our near neighbour, the lower floors were more soiled than usual, and the prisoners called out their dismay. I hated to pass by. I could hear the voice of Betty Hallett, who was often held for drunkenness, calling out in furious protest, 'Filth, filth, filth!'

'They should let them out,' Father said. 'At least until the mud has settled.' I knew Betty well, she was a kindly woman, when she had not taken too much of the drink.

'Drink is her demon,' Father said, as we heard that dreadful voice from behind the barred door and flinted walls, like the voice of a different person. I would go a long way to avoid it.

'I cannot bear the sound of her,' I said. I did not think, though, that because of the mud she should be released from the lock-up. If people commit a sin, then they must be punished.

'I'll race with you to the beach,' I said to Joseph.
(Even from down there I could hear her cries.)

We were meant to be following Father, in his walk
across the sands. We did not go westwards, the direction
the visitors mostly took, below the Rooms and on towards
the Cobb, past the bathing machines which clustered there
during the season. We walked instead Charmouth way,
and towards Black Ven. In the distance we could see a few
other figures – the tide was well out – walking or stooping
over the shore, or wandering under the smoky cliffs.

I thought I could see Sam Curtis, and also Mrs Dollin,
the neighbour who had bravely come to our rescue on the
night of the terrible storm. They were doing what Father
did: they were searching for curiosities.

Curiosities, that was what we called them, in the days
before I learned to know better. To the east of Lyme, the
cliffs were full of treasures. I didn't regard them as
treasures at first, just dull, dry shells and bones. Joe
never really came to care for them, though he tried his
utmost. We picked them up from the beach, or prised them
from the blue-grey cliff, which was the colour of the sea
on the blackest of days. It took skill, as the cliffs would
crumble at a touch – would sometimes crumble without
any touch at all. Father, like Sam Curtis and Nancy
Dollin, carried a little hammer on these excursions, with
which he tap, tap, tapped at the shifting cliffs.

Mostly, we found the bones of crocodiles, brown and
varnished-looking, or else the fossil fish we called turbot,
or the snake-stone ammonites, with their spiralling shells.

Visitors admired the ammonites in particular.
Sometimes they – the ladies and the gentlemen who came
to stay here after a season in Bath, where they took the
waters – would themselves stroll along the shore, the

Bathing machines clustered on the beach at Lyme.

ladies in their trailing skirts, trimmed with white fur as sullied as sandy snow. They would question us about the beach. They knew nothing about the changing tides.

'What do they want with such curiosities?' Joseph whispered to me.

I did not know. I only knew that they put them into cabinets, glass-fronted, such as Father sometimes made. We thought it madness, but we were ready to oblige, as we would be paid good money for our finds.

It was dull work, though, dry as shells and bones, and we dawdled along, scuffing through the sand, keeping an eye on Father in the distance. Mother barely consented to our helping, since she feared the cliff might fall.

Father was full of enthusiasm for the search, glad as always to be out of doors. 'Look at this!' he'd shout, striding across the sand to show us his hoard. He had found a lustrous handful of shells, a crocodile's verteberry – and the bones of some creature to us as yet unknown.

''Tis the teeth of a sea dragon,' Father said. 'They will look well in the shop.'

Our shop was set out in front of the cellar window. There we put a round table which Father had made, and on it we arranged our wares: the shells we thought two-a-penny, the fantastical bones, and other dry remains. They were mementoes of Lyme.

'M-mementoes.' Joe could not say the word, but it didn't matter. We enjoyed our days behind the counter. When the fishing had been good, we'd sell wet fish too: plump, fully-fleshed specimens seemingly still alive alongside the dried-out shells and bones.

'Would you care to buy a m..., a souvenir?' Joe asked any passing gentleman or lady. Many of the townspeople were letting out rooms to them. Mother declared that she would only let to decent, chapel-going folk so, since such as these had no time for holidays, we never found a lodger. We earned a small income by finding curiosities instead.

We put the money we earned in a polished brass box embossed with a picture of a ship in full sail. Mother, too, helped with the shop-keeping, though she thought our customers even madder than we did.

After giving them a curtsey, she waited impatiently until each one was out of earshot.

'What do they want with such nonsense?' she demanded. 'Shoards and popples, bits and pieces!' She would take their money all the same, and be glad to have it.

Chapter Five

WHEN WE WERE NOT on the beach, we were in the chapel, or so it now seems to me. We spent long hours – an eternity of hours! – bowed in our pew at Coombe Street Chapel. We had no opportunity to loll or to sleep, for the minister could see each and every one of us from his lofty, six-sided pulpit (each side affording him a different view).

I relished the stories from the Bible, of Daniel in the lions' den, or Jacob with his ladder, or Joseph with his many-coloured coat, and I listened to the sermons until my poor ears ached. But the prayers! The interminable and rambling prayers! By the time that a prayer was finished, I could no longer remember its beginning, and my knees were sore from kneeling on the bare wooden floor.

Mother frowned if she found us fidgeting. She even frowned if we coughed or sneezed. From the corner of my eye I could just see Joe, turning his head oh-so-slowly for a glimpse of the brass-fronted clock. The clock was set in the wall of the great gallery behind us, so we could not see what hour it was, could only hear the resounding tick, tick, tick. During very long prayers I would count the seconds, as they ticked so heavily away.

Joseph sat at the end of the row. Although we were not allowed to speak, I knew that he was not listening to a word that was being said. Yet he listened right enough when Old Curtis told his tales, tales which might have come straight from the holy book, of flood and fire and wreck. Most of all, Joe loved to hear the unhappy tale of the landing in Lyme of James, the Duke of Monmouth.

'My old grandfather told me this tale himself,' Sam Curtis said, 'and he was there when the young Duke landed.'

'He saw Monmouth!' Joseph said. Monmouth meant more to him than any Bible story.

'Everyone knows of Monmouth,' I interrupted. There were no memorials, no outward signs of his visit to Lyme, but nevertheless we all knew of Monmouth. Mother and Father, I expect, knew as much about him as old Sam Curtis.

'But they didn't *see* him,' Joseph objected.

'Only because they hadn't been born then. No more than you or I.' But I knew it was fruitless. In his mind's eye Joe was already marching with Monmouth.

More than a hundred years had passed since Monmouth and his tiny fleet had landed close by. He was raising a rebellion against the King his uncle, and he was well received that day in Lyme.

'A Monmouth! A Monmouth! The Protestant religion!' Joe was shouting, as the crowd had cried before him. The town had blossomed: the men decked their caps with green boughs, and the women strewed flowers at his feet. The old women were there too in their scarlet shawls (which flowed like a red river when they entered the chapel). Young children danced to a fiddler in the streets. Lyme seldom knew such a joyous occasion.

Rejoicing, though, was unhappily short. Monmouth and his humble army, ranged beneath their green and gold standard, marched off to Axminster in glory (and Joe

James Duke of Monmouth.

From an Original by Sir Peter Lely.

would willingly have marched away with them).

Just a few days later, on the sad and watery levels of Sedgemoor, the little, local, army came to grief. This was the last battle that has been fought on our English soil, and I hope it will ever remain so. Monmouth, defeated, was found hiding in a ferny ditch. He was taken away to London.

Punishment came, and came swiftly. Our part of the country was to pay dearly for trying to march against the King. The young Duke was beheaded, in London on Tower Hill. West Country men were to be tried by the hundred: twelve were executed in Lyme alone (though no horse could be found that would draw them to their fate). 'Tis said that Sam Curtis's grandfather had to go into hiding, because he had opened the doors of the Guildhall, as a welcome for the unlucky Duke.

I was glad that Joe could never be given a chance to march with Monmouth. He would surely have been killed in the battle or (worse) on the makeshift gallows at Monmouth beach: a thirteenth victim of that terrible revenge.

''Twas an exciting time,' was all that Joe said, as he went on day-dreaming through the service in the chapel.

When chapel was over, we remained sitting for our lessons. It was here, between services and sometimes in the evenings, that we learnt to read and write.

'What was the text?' Joseph whispered to me, as we waited for the adults to leave. Mother (or Father more rarely) would randomly ask us questions, checking whether our attention had wandered. Joe relied on me for information against such an event.

> *Heaven and earth shall pass away: but my words*
> *shall not pass away*
> *But of that day and that hour knoweth no man...*

I chanted under my breath as the boots clacked out.
For Sunday school, we children sat in rows in the pews,
and read in turn from the leather-bound Bible. This was
how we learned our letters, our A B C. (All good
Christians must be able to read the Bible.)

So often had I read how God created the world in seven
days that I could recite the account without so much as a
glance at the text – and this Joe had noticed.

'Speak, parrot,' he murmured as my reading began.
He was quicker at reading than I was, but still I learnt in
time, and from reading I taught myself to write (and now I
have come to write this, my book).

Yet for a long while reading was to me just another
form of labour. I did not need to read the Bible, since
I knew so much of it by heart. I could not have imagined
that I would ever want to read any other book.

CHAPTER SIX

AS WELL AS I KNEW the scriptures, I knew the shore, the cliffs and the strange tides of Lyme Regis, where the waters would sometimes stand at the turn for an hour or more. We spent a good deal of our time around Lyme Bay. I knew the cliff road too: the road to Charmouth which began at Long Entry, below the church. But as I went no further, my knowledge went no further.

So I well remember the day we walked along the river as far as Uplyme, on an outing as rare as it was memorable. We did not have holidays in the way the ladies and the gentlemen did; unless we were ill, we worked, or went to school and chapel.

The sun shone brightly on that day – or it does in my memory. We were exploring, Joe and I, following our river of many names. We began at the Buddle, at the mouth of the river, where it flowed darkly under town bridge and on into the sands. Here, the waters were almost black, channelled by houses and choked with chesil. As we began up Coombe Street, the water was hidden by the houses, glimpsed only through the passages which reached through the houses from front to back.

I remember what we were saying as we walked along. We were talking about the fish.

'What do the river fish do, when they meet the sea?'
Joe asked. 'They surely can't abide the salt.'
'River water's salty too,' I said. 'So close to the sea.'
'Oh no, it isn't,' Joe said at once. 'And don't argify.
Come.' He led me through a drangway and down steps to
the river, running fast and foamy to its fate.
'Drink,' Joe commanded. I knelt and scooped a handful
of water. Joe was right: the water tasted not of salt, but of
earth.
'Well, anyways,' I said, 'some fish can swim in salt or
fresh.'
As if to prove my point, a clutch of ducks, with a single
duckling, half-grown and fussy, swam calmly under the
low stone arches which separated river from sea.
'Salt *and* fresh,' I said.
Joe fell silent, and I stopped talking too. We were passing Mill Green, a place where we'd been forbidden to ven-
ture. If Joe or I were ever foul-mouthed or shifty, Mother
would warn us, 'you'll end up in Mill Green.'
I was relieved to see that there was no one about,
except for an old piebald dog, flopped out in the road.
Everyone, the men, the women and the children, were all
at work, mostly in the mill. It was noisy here, and the
looms were clacking.
We walked swiftly past, and swifter still, now we had
come to Jericho. Here, safely out of Lyme, lived many
members of the Baptist sect, and here, until quite recently,
believers had been baptised in the river, which they nick-
named the Jordan. The cottages clung close to the water's
edge, and faces watched us from upstairs windows.
Beyond Jericho, the mills were mostly silent. There
wasn't so much cloth made in Lyme as previously. We
passed by another mill. This one was empty, save for

a family who'd occupied the uppermost floor. Their youngest, a boy I think, came hurtling out of the door to look at us. His mother followed, and offered us a cup of that same earthy water (from the river now called the Lym). I drank thankfully, thirstily.

By now I felt I was surely in foreign parts. I had only known of Mill Green, and the bordering Baptists. It was so peaceful hereabouts: the river flowed steadily, and low. We waded easily through it to reach the fields. Fish seemed plentiful, and Joe tried to catch them in his hands. The cows in the fields we came to were far fatter than those which cropped the cliff-top turf.

We flapped our wings like birds, and ran across the meadows, free for once from the ever-encroaching tides.

'Shall we eat some of our food?' Joe asked hungrily. He was carrying the satchel which held it, the bread and the apples we'd brought for our meal.

We lay back on the grass. Trees reared above us, their leaves a brilliant scarlet, yellow, or brown as nuts. Our heads were cleared of the sound of the sea. The country was very quiet. In truth, when I listened I could hear no sound at all.

'Can we rest a little longer?' I pleaded, as I noticed Joe's fidgeting. 'We must be almost at the village.'

Uplyme was our destination – and that of many other children, who could be seen approaching, in groups or one by one, from each and every direction.

We were all going to the Uplyme inn. At harvest time, a celebration was held there. Crossing the last field, we walked down gloomy Black Dog Lane. We thought we could smell the pies as we drew close. The innkeeper's wife always baked these pies, special-like, at the start of the season. They were hartberry pies, of pastry filled with

The view across the fields to Uplyme.

juicy, purplish fruit, sweet–sour, with crusty, clotted, cream. 'Twas no wonder we children walked miles for them.

We gathered outside the inn, a greedy horde of us, waiting for the innkeeper's wife, brown and laughing, to open the door.

Here she was – with her wooden tray, stacked with warm and dripping pies.

'No pushing,' she ordered, as we all reached up, trying not to be seen to jostle. A pie in each hand, Joe and I turned homeward, our mouths full, our faces livid with all the juices.

We were content. There was a murmur of voices, as the other children moved off in other directions, some of them singing (if their mouths weren't too full) songs of harvest and repletion.

Joe began to speak, his mouth still crammed. Seeing I did not understand his words, instead he pointed.

'Look,' he was saying. 'Look.' When at last I looked I saw Sam Curtis, down along the hedgerow, gathering sloes.

We weren't so far from home after all.

CHAPTER SEVEN

W E RETURNED TO LYME by a different road, and
I believe that Sam Curtis never once saw us.
Our supper was ready, waiting for us when we arrived
back at home.

'I'm hungry,' Joseph said to Mother, as he pulled off
his coat.

I cast my eyes around for Father.

'We won't wait for your father,' Mother said.
'He's away over the cliffs to Charmouth. He's hunting
curiosities again.'

I knew that Mother thought Father spent too much time
on the shore. She preferred carpentry, which she thought
more respectable.

Joe had begun to drink his onion broth. He dipped a
crumbling heel of bread into it.

Mother didn't sit down. She stirred, stirred at the pot
of broth on the fire.

'When will Father be home?' I asked.

'He'll be here before dark,' Mother said. I looked out
of the window. It wouldn't be dark for another hour or so.

We sat by the fire and waited. By now the sky was
darker than the sea. But still Father did not come.

He came when we were up in our beds, though we
were not asleep. Two fishermen were carrying him.

'I don't see how he could've a-fallen,' one fisherman (Mrs Dollin's son, George) was saying. 'He knew the cliffs as well as he knew his own self. There must have been a landslip.'

We gathered round Father as he lay downstairs. He was still breathing, though his breath came awkward-like. Mother was rubbing his hands to warm them.

Then Father opened his eyes and blinked, as if the light were painful.

'Father,' I whispered, 'are you well enough to speak?'

Father gave a small, stiff nod, and closed his eyes again.

We were never to learn the truth of it. In the days that followed, Father grew weak and worsened. The fall brought on a terrible cough, which Mother called consumption. We tried to make him easy. We brought him comfortable stuff – wine we had begged from our landlord – but 'twas against his beliefs to drink it.

We built huge fires of driftwood, and burned up all the candles too.

Yet every action was in vain. My father died, quite peacefully, while we were watching by his side.

'What will we do without you, Father?' I cried. 'What will I do without you?'

CHAPTER EIGHT

Then the time of our woes began.

NOW THAT FATHER HAD GONE, we found we had very little money (save that which Mother earned from her lace-making). We did not care to go curiosity-hunting any more, and in any case Mother would not hear of it.

We began to strip the house bare of possessions. We sold our candlesticks, we sold all but one of our saucepans, we sold Father's wood-working tools. Soon we would be forced to sell the very covers from our beds.

Then, one morning, Mother called us to her and said, 'I can see no end to this selling-up. I have made up my mind to go to the Parish.'

Mother was a proud woman; she did not want to take charity. The Parish men doled out money to the poor and needy, but they were strict, terrible strict at times.

'I'm not afraid of their questions,' Mother said. She left us waiting by our fire – the sea at least had been kind to us, and we had coals and wood in plenty.

We sat by the fire and waited. There had been so much waiting lately, so much silence in the house, without Father's whistling and the banging of his hammer. None of us went into the cellar any more, only the sea made its gentle intrusion when the tide was standing high.

The door slammed. Mother came rushing up the stairs.

'They've granted us five shillings,' she cried. 'They believed my words.'

That night we ate beef, with potatoes and white bread instead of black. The meat fitted, just, into the one small pot which remained to us, but tasted none-the-worse for its tight confinement.

Mother fell asleep straight after supper like one who has been released. But her relief scarce outlasted the week (and the meat). The Parish granted us no more money. We were back to bare boards.

It was then that Mother made the decision which I found hardest of all to accept. She called me to her, saying, 'Mary, I have decided. There is a vacancy for a girl and we have no money. I'm sending you to work in the mill.'

So I was sent to work at Mill Green, the place we had always shunned, a place we'd been told decent people never visited. I went out in the morning while it was still dark, passed the grand expanse of our chapel – and entered the mill. I could hear the noise long before I could see the building, the constant clatter above which you could only hear the loudest shout.

The looms filled – crammed – the ground floor of the mill: my job was to move amongst them, sweeping mainly, sweeping the fluff which choked the floors, dodging the ever-shifting, noisy looms.

After half an hour of such work, I felt sure it must be evening. Weariness soon made my eyes water, and the weavers were not kind to me.

'This is no place for moping children,' one of them said. 'Why don't you run away home to your Mother?'

In truth I would have loved to take this scornful advice. My head was dull and aching.

'Oh, leave the girl be,' said another voice, more kindly. 'She'll get used to the work by and by.'

The voice (I knew it at once) was Betty Hallett's.

To sink so low that I had to work with a drunkard, even suffer her kindness! Yet the thought reproached me, and I could not help but be grateful.

The day passed, more slowly than a sermon. In my memory that day has scarcely shortened. Night was coming as I returned to our house.

I was desperate. I sobbed and wailed as I had never done at the funeral of my dear father. Mother did not reprove me for the excess of my grief. How, I thought, could she so turn against her younger child as to send her to that mill?

Mother sat in silence. 'You will understand when you are older,' she said (though I have yet to understand). She took my hand. 'I will not send you again, Mary,' she promised.

My sobs dwindled. I rubbed my eyes, wiped my nose and glanced around me.

'Where is Joe?' I asked.

Mother shrugged. 'He's down on the seashore, the disobedient boy. He's as bad as your father ever was – and I only hope he stays away from the cliffs. He denies that he's going in search of curiosities, but what else could he be a-doing?'

I thought I would go and see.

CHAPTER NINE

I WENT DOWN TO THE SEASHORE to look for Joe, to see
what he was planning. I was glad, too, of the fresh,
clear air, after a choked day in the mill. Beneath the
bridge, the Buddle waters, dusky and haunted, were
seeping into the sands under the cover of approaching
night. I ran rapidly away across the shore, where the
evening light still lingered.

The day was at its lowest, and I thought wistfully of
my father, hoping to see him again, if only for a moment.
I could see a shape ahead of me, which I thought must be
Joe, and suddenly I needed his company. I stared at the
shore: it wasn't a post, or a sea-wracked tree; the shape
was moving. It must be Joe. He was digging fast and
furious along the untidy high-tide line.

As I advanced, he threw down his spade, and began
scrabbling in his hole like a dog. The hole was a deep
one, and stretched a long way. He must have been
digging for some hours.

As I came closer I could hear his breath, heavy from all
his labours. 'What are you doing, Joe?' I demanded,
looking down into his trench.

'I'm looking for treasure,' Joe said. I thought he spoke
a little reluctantly.

'Treasure?'

'I'm searching for Monmouth's gold,' Joe said defiantly.

Monmouth's gold. I might have guessed it. When Monmouth landed at Lyme Regis, some anxious townspeople, fearing an outbreak of disorder, had buried their gold and their silver, their rings and trinkets, for safety in the ground. Handfuls of these valuables, long forgotten, had been found when a house was demolished or (more often) when a building fell into the street. Other coins and jewellery had been found on the beach.

'Fool's gold, more likely,' I said in disgust.

''Tis true I haven't found anything as yet,' Joe had to admit. 'But I will soon, don't you fear.' He went on digging, a maddened dog, causing sand to fly in all directions.

He would not stop. He went on digging even though he must have seen that night was hastening on. I was unwilling to leave him at his solitary, fruitless task. I wandered aimlessly along the sands.

Then old habit took hold of me, and I walked towards the cliffs, stumbling a little on the weed-covered rocks.

I stumbled, it might be said, upon the ammonite. I wasn't at that moment, searching – I was weary, and night had come. Fossils reminded me too keenly of Father, and I was discouraged, too, by Mother's growing disapproval of the pursuit.

The ammonite, a handsome specimen, came out of the cliff as cleanly as a tooth. Carefully I carried it, in my arms, towards Joe. He had by now abandoned his excavations, and sat gloomily on the sand.

'I've found a sea-serpent, Joe,' I began.

He did not so much as glance at my find and I did not dare to repeat my words.

'I'm going to try looking in the Buddle,' Joe said. In winter, in the fine black gravel at the river's mouth, you could find pins sometimes, or tiny brass coins, amongst the broken-down shells and other debris.

'We won't be able to see anything. It's too dark,' I objected. 'You can scarcely see your hand in front of your face.'

Truth to tell, I was afraid we might catch a glimpse of something. I dreaded the Buddle mouth at such a time, and usually avoided going anywhere near. We all knew about the lost soul haunting the river.

Once I had seen her, the lady who haunted the river at this its darkest place, overhung by houses and bridge. I never wanted to see her again.

It happened like this. I had been sent by my mother to buy some eggs: half a dozen I think it was. The woman who sold the eggs had a little wooden hut close by the Cobb. I took the eggs and paid for them, and put them in my pocket.

Then I stayed to watch a timber ship unload its cargo of tall Russian trees, and I did not leave till the work was over.

I was late, I ran along the Walk and an egg came flying from my pocket, bursting in a yellow mess as the egg hit the ground.

Then I was afraid to go home and be scolded. Hardly noticing where I was, I reached the mouth of the Buddle and waited. Waited for what? Not for what I saw.

I saw the lady, a moony Pope of a thing, standing in the water, on the landward side of the bridge. Her hair was black, and hung around her shoulders, her face was white as frost. She looked, I thought, straight through me, as she opened her mouth and chanted, like someone performing an old song.

I rue the time
I sold water for wine
And combed my hair of a Sunday.

She was destined, it was said, to stay there forever, to walk but a cock's stride a year along the river, chanting her sorrowful song. I never wanted to see her again.

Perhaps Joe feared her also, for he marched straight up the steps from the shore without uttering a single protest.

CHAPTER TEN

THE AMMONITE WAS HEAVY, and I tottered a little under its weight, as I tried to run after Joe.

'Joe! Wait for me!' I shouted, afraid that the ghostly figure might, with her slow cock's stride, drift after me up the steps. I managed not to drop my treasure all the same, and Mother sighed when she saw it. She had been standing anxiously at the door.

'Don't bring that object into the house,' she ordered. Obediently, I left my stone outside, on our empty shop table, and went upstairs to my bed.

Freed from the mill, I was directed by my mother the next morning to help her clean the house. Up in our first-floor room, I had abandoned the polishing, and was feeding an apple to our poor neglected horse, which now was left to rock alone. I stroked, as I always used to, the horse's wooden nose.

There came a knock at the downstairs door, and I ran to open it. Outside was a lady, a late-lingering visitor, her face half-hidden by a smart grey bonnet.

'Good morning,' said the lady.

'Good morning, ma'am,' I said, bobbing my head.

She pointed with her well-gloved hand to my ammonite still lying on the table.

'I should like,' the lady said, 'to buy the curiosity you have there.'

This unexpected visitor surprised me, and I did not know what to say. The lady, meanwhile, took my reluctance as an unwillingness to sell.

'Come now,' she coaxed, 'I'll pay you half a crown for it.'

'Half a crown!' I said. I was as pleased as Punch.

'Why, certainly ma'am,' I said, 'If you could just wait for one moment, I will fetch my brother to carry the curiosity home for you.'

I watched them go: the lady with her bonnet and her beautiful gloves, and Joe following a few paces behind, grinning in disbelief.

So the curiosity-hunting started again, and we went daily down to the beach, sent with our mother's blessing. The Curtis and Dollin families were generally a-searching too. (You could hear Nancy Dollin from a long way off, with her loud and yaffling laugh.) Few visitors were seen upon the shore, now that the season was over.

I never did see the ghost-woman again. Only the once did I see her, and that was when I was a young child. Maybe children were the only ones to see her – and my childhood had vanished (I felt) the day Father fell from the cliff. Nowadays I wandered the shore with Joe, picking up shells and shards and bones, for Mother to sell in our shop. (We had moved the table inside the cellar these cold winter days.)

There had been a great storm, and the tide had run high (they said that seaweed draped the cobbles all up along Broad Street). A sea-fret was obscuring Lyme Bay, in wanton patches, isolating the shore. Joe was further off, treasure-hunting like as not, and I was standing in the mists of silence when a sudden noise disturbed me.

I looked across to where our harbour, the Cobb, could be momentarily seen like a stone-sickle in the sea.

I heard the sound again.

'I thought I heard a cow,' I told myself, 'a cow lowing in the midst of the water.'

Nancy Dollin's grandmother, before she died, used to tell of how she could remember a spit of land which stretched out hereabouts, rivalling the Cobb. Once cows had grazed on that green earth, where now (the mist had cleared a little and I could see a ship) they were transported over a greener sea. I stared at sea and ship until they dazzled me, danced in front of my eyes. I thought I saw some curly clusters of horns, low-lying in the water.

The ship moved out to sea, parting from the Cobb, and bound no doubt for Guernsey, whose ports were being blockaded then (for we were at war) by Napoleon's sailors.

I felt bereft. I wondered where Joe was. Could he be treasure-hunting again? He still nursed hopes of a discovery. 'Then we could all be comfortable again,' Joe said.

'It was the sea-serpent that brought us money,' I reminded him. Joe stared back, and went on digging. He picked up every shard or bone he found, but they weren't what he really was wanting.

Yet I must confess that it was Joe who made the first find. The cattle-ship was on the horizon, the tide was moving swiftly in and we found ourselves by the cliffs. Watching the sea, I had moved further down the beach, Charmouth-way, than I'd intended. The sea had drawn me in that direction.

Joe was holding Father's hammer, tap-tapping at the cliffs like a misplaced woodpecker. His tapping was aimless, random to my ear, until he began again, with almost the speed of that demented bird.

I went to see what he was doing. As I approached, the empty socket of an eye, huge and round, seemed to stare at me from the rocks. Joe was tracing the outline of a massive bony head.

'What ever can it be?' I whispered.

'I don't rightly know,' Joe said. 'Not definitely.'

I stared at the creature's snappish snout. 'It looks to me,' I said, 'as if we've found a crocodile.'

''Tis far too big for us to handle the whole of it,' Joe said. I saw the incoming tide, the thickening mist, and I could not help but agree.

'A c–crocodile,' Joe said. ''Tis best perhaps to let such bones alone.' We had never seen a whole creature before, just here and there teeth, or some verteberries.

As we walked away, each holding one end of our discovery, I at my end, facing backwards, could see behind us that elongated skeleton, headless now, and outlined in the rocks.

CHAPTER ELEVEN

CURTISES AND DOLLINS came running from the rocks
around, to help us carry our crocodile skull.

''Tiddn't a bad little specimen,' Sam Curtis said,
panting a little under its weight. 'You'll probably get a
few shillings for it.'

'We're going to keep it,' I said. I hadn't consulted Joe,
but he was nodding in agreement.

'Keep it!' said Old Curtis – and that was what Mother
said too when we told her.

Word got around about our find which (despite
Mother's protests) we had placed in the first-floor room,
a companion for the horse. The juxtaposition was
worrying to Joe.

'That horse will rock and rear in such company!' he
objected, and at his words I seemed to see the horse's eye
roll. The sight of the crocodile's snout had terrified him.

Joe moved the skull down into the cellar, where one of
the Misses Philpot must have noticed it – for a few days
later the maid came calling.

'Miss Philpot would like you to visit her,' she told me.

There were three Misses Philpot, that much I knew, and
I wasn't sure whether I could tell them apart. They lived
up at the top of the town in Silver Street, in a large
thatched house. I had never been inside it, not even on
one of Father's errands.

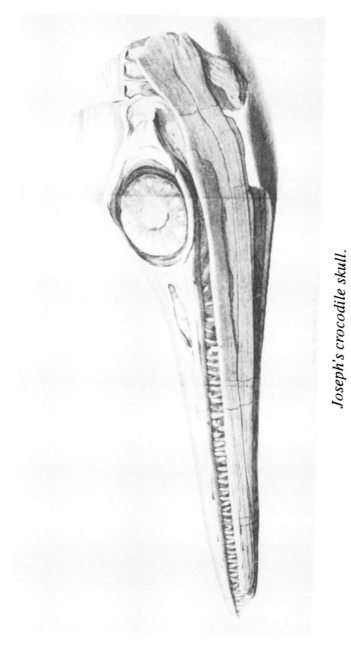

Joseph's crocodile skull.

I knew that at least one of them went curiosity-hunting.
I'd heard they had a fossil collection in their house, and
I'd seen them on the beach. Unlike some of the ladies
(and some of the gentlemen) they were serious collectors,
not just a-dabbling like estuary ducks. They'd bought one
or two pieces from us as well.

'I will not sell the crocodile,' I said. The skull, with its
rigid bone eye, was lodged on the window-sill, overlook-
ing the sea in which it once had swam, cleaving the waters
with its long and powerful snout.

The creature was dead indeed, but some of its power
remained, and I could feel the strength of it.

Spring had come at last, and summer. We eked out our
living selling serpents, and angels' wings, and masses of
pearly shells, but we did not sell our crocodile skull.

I had been invited to visit the Misses Philpot, and
expected that they would try to make a purchase, but
I had mistaken their intentions.

I stood in the hallway, looking down at my boots,
which seemed over-large and grubby on the oriental
carpet. (Boulders from the beach.) I was directed to the
sitting-room where a fire was burning, even though 'twas
July, and warm too.

'Ah, Mary,' said Miss Philpot. This Miss Philpot was
the smallest and prettiest of the sisters (I suddenly realised)
and the keenest fossil-hunter.

I was seated on an upright chair, my feet tucked
carefully underneath, and the maid was pouring tea.

I sipped politely. The tea was too hot for me, but I
wanted to drink quickly, before I spilt it.

'I've noticed, Mary,' Miss Philpot continued,
'how much time you are spending on the beach.'

'Yes, ma'am,' I said surprised. Did she disapprove?

'You seem,' Miss Philpot said, 'to enjoy your discoveries as much as I do mine.'

I'd never really thought about it. ''Twas exciting finding the crocodile, ma'am,' I said at last. I looked shyly at her, wondering if she'd ever made such a find herself.

Miss Philpot beckoned me across to the cupboard, in which she had laid out her finds, each one labelled, dated in a neat and tiny hand.

I put down my empty cup, glad to move closer to the window. The fire was causing my face to turn scarlet. When I began to examine Miss Philpot's collection, I realised she had many specimens I'd never seen before. Perhaps there was no end to the wealth of the sea.

After my first visit, I returned quite often. Miss Philpot talked to me of all her pieces, and we puzzled over them.

'No one is sure what some of these creatures were,' Miss Philpot said. 'Perhaps one day we will know.' Sometimes she asked me questions about the fossils. I was proud when I knew the answers, and was able to add some knowledge of my own.

More rarely, Miss Philpot called at our house, where she never failed to admire the crocodile skull.

'It's a real pity you were forced to leave the creature's body behind,' Miss Philpot said.

'We could not go back,' I replied, and that was the truth. We had meant to return, but when we tried we found that part of the shore could not be reached, on account of the bad weather. High tides and rock falls made the spot inaccessible.

'We will have to wait till next winter, ma'am,' I said, 'and hope that the storms will uncover that part of the shore again.'

CHAPTER TWELVE

THE SUMMER SEASON was advancing. Each year there seemed to be more visitors staying in our town, lodging in rooms where white curtains flapped at open windows, revealing small heaps of pebbles and shells on every other window-sill.

The visitors were often customers at our shop. Some of them understood about fossils – some corresponded regularly with Miss Philpot – some would become excited at the discovery of a dog's cast-off bone.

The shore had by now become my second home. Most days I was down there, my face brown as a nut (and nuts would soon be ripening on the banks of the Lym), my boots forever salt-stained. Joe accompanied me less and less: he seemed to be losing interest in collecting.

'You will find it for me, Mary,' he said. 'You will find the skeleton by and by.' Joe was soon to be apprenticed to an upholsterer, and his head was full of this new life.

'I'll no longer have the time for curiosity-hunting,' Joseph said.

'Nor treasure–hunting, neither,' I muttered in reply.

I awoke early on the day of the storm. I was excited, because I realised what the onset of winter weather might mean. The wind and the rain were beating and baying around the house (and still the crocodile watched impassively,

with his stony, vacant eye). The waves, too, reared thick
and foamy, hissing like dragons at our house.

I lay listening to the storm, listening to its progress.
When the wind dropped, in a sudden way, I dressed
quickly and left the house, just as the tide began to ebb.
The day was bitter-cold, and the icy sky was etched in
small, sharp snow. Snow soon smarted the sand, salting
the yellow grains.

My clenched fingers felt like sticks of frost as I trudged
along, ducking my head against the freezing air and
kicking at the driftwood thrown high along the tideline.
The lightly-bleached wood was darkened by wet flakes as
the snow merged upon it.

The walk seemed endless. From time to time I raised
my face (to have it slapped in the icy air) and looked ahead
for my landmark. For I had memorised where the
crocodile lay. High on the cliff, above his lair, there grew
a great thorn tree, scarlet now, and festooned with berries.
Landward, I turned.

As I hoped, the storm had re-opened that part of the
cliff. I began to run until I stood, tight up against the
rock, directly under the tree.

I had Father's fossil hammer in my pocket, cold against
my colder fingers. With it, I tapped, tapped, tapped at that
part of Black Ven cliff, under the thorn tree, until I found
an edge of the skeleton again. I traced the outline
painstakingly.

I had found it again, and I'd thought no further.
The crocodile lay at the foot of the cliff, with a full weight
of rock above it. I could not prise it out alone. I would
have to go for help.

Mother was still in her bed when I reached home: a rare
sight indeed.

'Whatever is the matter?' she demanded, brushing her hair back from her sleepy eyes. When she heard my news though, she woke up at once.

The skeleton was ours by rights, since we already had the skull. We did not fear robbery – except by the sea, which might at any time cover the site again. We had to act quickly.

Mother ran out of the door. A stone's throw away, in Coombe Street, two men were working on a house, and she took a good look at them. She knew them both by sight – and they knew something of the beach. She hired them for the day to dig out the skeleton.

I, too, helped direct the digging, through I could hardly bear to watch. Suppose in their haste they made a slip, damaging the crocodile beyond repair?

Behind me, many other people were watching, despite the bitter cold and the fall of snow. They lit fires on the beach and gathered round them, talking and watching, watching and talking. They gasped, applauded when the crocodile (as long as three grown men) was laid across the whitening sand.

Everyone in Lyme was talking about the find – and so were people in places more distant. On November 9th, 1812, the *Western Flying Post* reported our discovery. I read the report aloud to my mother:

> *A few days ago, immediately after the late high tide, was discovered, under the cliffs between Lyme Regis and Charmouth, the complete petrifaction of a crocodile, 17 feet in length, in a very perfect state. It was dug out of the cliff nearly on a level with the sea, about 100 feet below the surface of the earth.*

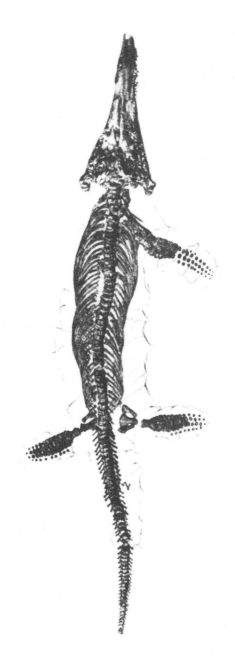

' ... the complete petrification of a crocodile, 17 feet in length.'

''Tis *very* perfect,' Mother said, gazing at the skeleton (now with skull restored). The crocodile was occupying one whole floor of our house, carried there in triumph from the shore. ''Tis very large, also. Whatever shall we do with it?'

I wanted to keep the crocodile. Sometimes at night I would come down from my bedroom to look at the skeleton, stretched out in silvered state under the moon. I did not want it alive again, but I did want to know how the creature had lived and moved and had its being. I wanted to know everything about our solitary lodger.

We were never, though, to have a lodger for long. Our landlord came and bought him from us. The front door banged, and in came Mr Henley. He looked long and hard at the crocodile, unblinking. He handed us money (£23-0-0), and he took our lodger away.

Even Mother was rather sorry to see him go, though we were all glad of the money (and of the space).

'Maybe one day you'll find another such creature,' Mother said, to comfort me. 'There's as many curiosities in that cliff as there are fish in the sea.'

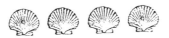

Bullock's Museum of Natural History.

CHAPTER THIRTEEN

I AM OLDER NOW, and I have found my mother's words to be true. There are as many curiosities on the shore as there are fish in the sea. I have discovered many a curiosity upon the cliffs and beaches of Lyme, and my name has become famous both in these parts, and far across the land. Indeed, kings of countries way over the sea have made journeys to visit me. Hunting curiosities – and advising those who came seeking this place so rich in fossils – that has become my life.

My crocodile did not rest long in the hands of Mr Henley. 'Twas transported to London, to the capital of England, to a great museum in the wide and stately street they call Piccadilly.

I never saw the place (which was called Bullock's Museum of Natural History), but I have heard tell of it often enough, and I can picture it in my mind's eye.

My crocodile was exhibited in a vast, vast room, lit from above by a lofty dome. Fantastic feathery trees grew up into the room, entwined with spitting serpents, and crowned with a Paradisical bird. The palm trees waved their branches over creatures the like of which I have never seen. There was an ostrich, a tusky elephant, a rhinoceros, a mammoth (or so I have been told). They stood, stuffed, in their enclosure, for all the world to see.

On the walls behind them were hung the weapons with which these wild beasts were hunted: spears, shields and vicious daggers from Africa and the Indies; and a mask like the face of evil. A knight, clad in full armour, rode the room on his horse.

Glass cabinets lined the lower walls, like those the ladies and gentlemen used for their specimens in Lyme. They contained fish and stalking birds.

The room was filled with marvels, but for me the greatest of these was still the skeleton which I, Mary Anning, found on the snow-swept beach. I know now that my find was not really a crocodile, but an *ichthyosaurus*, a fish lizard, a very important specimen – and ancient too. It was year upon year old.

My crocodile (as I still thought it) was displayed across one long wall, over the heads of the jungle beasts, a wonder and a glory in the London sun. It had been drawn from the cliff in snow and firelight – from the rocks in Lyme Regis, under Black Ven.

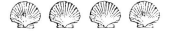